Usborne

100 things
to
make & do

D0253716

Contents

Scaly dinosaurs

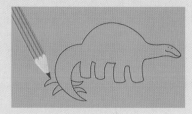

1. Use a pencil to draw the outline of a dinosaur's body on green paper. Then, add eyes, a mouth, spikes on its tail, and toenails.

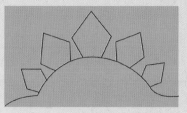

2. Draw a bony plate in the shape of a diamond in the middle of the back. Then, draw smaller plates on both sides of the middle one.

3. Draw over your pencil lines with a felt-tip pen. Add rows of U-shaped scales along the body. Then, add teeth with correcting fluid.

4. Draw lines on the bony plates. Then, draw lots of little lines on the spikes and toenails. Fill in parts of the dinosaur.

5. For a dinosaur with a frill, draw several curved lines along its back. Then, join the ends of the lines with wavy lines, like this.

Paper lanterns

1. Fold a piece of thick paper in half. Then, cut along the fold to make two rectangles. Each rectangle can be used to make a lantern.

2. Fold one rectangle in half so that the long sides meet. Make cuts into the folded side, but don't cut all the way up to the top.

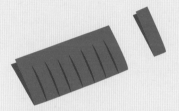

Spread the glue on this edge.

3. When you reach the end of the paper, cut all the way to the top, to make a narrow strip. This will be the handle for the lantern.

4. Open out the folded piece of paper. Spread glue along one of the short edges, then press it firmly onto the other short edge.

Glue the handle onto the inside.

5. Spread glue on both ends of the strip that you cut off in step 3. Press the ends firmly onto the top of the lantern. Let the glue dry.

6. Make another lantern from the other rectangle of paper. Then, decorate both lanterns with stickers, glitter glue or paper shapes.

Ice castle collage

Glue the mountains along the bottom edge.

Make the road narrow at the top.

1. For mountains, cut pink paper triangles of different sizes. Make one of them much bigger than the others.

2. Cut the tip off the big triangle. Glue the mountains onto a blue piece of paper. Add the big one last.

3. Draw a wiggly shape for a road on pale pink paper. Cut it out, then glue it onto the big mountain.

4. Cut out three tall towers and a wall. Glue them on, then cut out and glue on two short towers.

5. Cut a shiny paper door, windows and roofs. Glue them on. Add tiny windows with a silver pen.

6. Draw bricks. Then outline the bricks and windows with a silver pen. Glue on shiny sequins, too.

7. Pour some glitter and granulated sugar into a container, then shake it to mix everything together.

8. Dab white glue on the road, roofs and mountains. Pour the sugar mixture on. Shake off any excess.

9. Cut out a moon from kitchen foil and glue it on. Press silver star stickers onto the sky, too.

Tissue paper face

1. Cut a rectangle out of tissue paper. Glue it onto white cardboard and draw an oval on it.

2. Tear a piece of tissue paper the size of your oval. Glue the tissue over the oval.

3. Tear a rectangle for the shoulders. Glue it so that it overlaps the oval, like this.

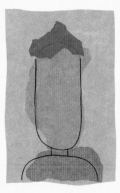

4. Tear a rough shape of tissue paper for the hair. Glue it at the top of the oval.

5. When the glue is dry, draw around the face. Add some lines for the body and neck.

6. Use a pen to draw wavy hair. Add ears, eyes, eyebrows, a nose and a mouth.

Scary fish picture

1. Mix thick red and white paints to make pink, then paint two overlapping curves with a thick paintbrush.

2. When the paint is dry, use a white pencil to outline the brushstrokes. Add lines for the fins and the tail, too.

3. Dip the end of a strip of thin cardboard into thick white paint, then print a row of teeth on each jaw.

4. Finger paint spots with pale pink paint, then add a white eye. When the paint is dry, add a black dot in the eye.

5. For a smaller fish, paint a curved brushstroke with a thick paintbrush, lifting the brush off quickly at the end.

6. Add an outline and details with a white pencil. Finger paint a white eye. When the paint is dry, add a black dot.

Pecking hens

1. Fold a paper plate in half. Crease the fold well. Open it out, then paint the back of the plate.

2. Fold the plate in half again. For a beak, cut a triangle from paper and glue it into the fold.

3. Cut some triangles from bright paper. These will be the spikes on top of the hen's head.

4. Glue the spikes to the back of the plate. Cut out circles of paper and glue them on for eyes.

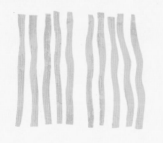 

5. Cut bright tissue paper into lots of thin strips as long as your hand. Gather the strips into a bunch.

6. Twist the strips together at one end. Tape them on for a tail. Rock the hens to make them peck.

Tulip card

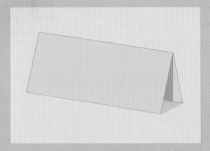

1. To make a card, fold a piece of thick yellow paper in half, with its long edges together. Then, press firmly along the fold.

2. Draw tulip shapes on bright paper and cut them out. Then, draw the same number of stalks on green paper and cut them out.

3. Glue the stalks at different heights onto the card. Make them overlap the bottom edge. Then, trim off the ends, like this.

4. Spread glue over the backs of the tulips. Then, press them onto the ends of the stalks, making some of them overlap each other.

Flower collage

1. Rip some long strips of blue tissue paper. Glue them across a piece of paper, so that they overlap. Let the glue dry.

2. Cut some thin strips of green tissue paper for stems and glue them along the bottom of the paper.

3. Cut out lots of rounded petals from red tissue paper. Glue four petals at the top of some of the stems.

4. Cut out orange petals, too. Glue them at the top of other stems, so that some overlap the red petals.

5. Use a thin black felt-tip pen to draw around each petal. You don't need to follow the edges exactly.

6. Draw a small circle in the middle of each flower, then add two or three lines on each petal.

Snowflake giftwrap

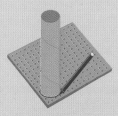

1. Put a cardboard tube on a piece of sponge cloth and draw around it with a pen. If you don't have a tube, use a small jar lid.

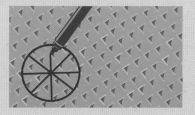

2. Using the pen, draw an 'X' shape inside the circle, touching the edges. Then, add a '+' over the top, to make a snowflake shape.

3. To make a snowflake, cut out the circle. Then, cut little triangles from between the lines, but don't cut all the way to the middle.

Spread the glue on the side that you drew on.

4. Lay the cardboard tube on a piece of cardboard and draw around it. Cut out the circle, then glue on the snowflake with white glue.

If you don't have a cork, use a plastic bottle top instead.

5. Spread white glue on one end of a cork. Press the cork onto the middle of the cardboard circle, then leave the glue to dry completely.

Let the paper dry before using it to wrap gifts.

6. Holding the cork, dip the snowflake into thick white paint. Press it onto a big piece of thin paper, then print lots more snowflakes.

Patterned birds

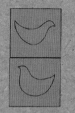

1. Draw two squares on a piece of brown giftwrap. Then, use a pencil to draw a simple outline of a bird in each square, like this.

2. Paint one bird pink and the other black. Then, paint the squares black and blue. Don't worry if a little of the paper shows through the paint.

3. When the paint is completely dry, draw a square around the pink bird with blue chalk pastels. Then, add some patterns.

4. Add legs and feet, and outline the body with a pale chalk pastel. Then, use a bright pastel to add lines on the bird and in the square.

5. Use a dip pen and black ink, or a black felt-tip pen, to add an eye, beak and lines on the body. Paint some black spots, too.

6. Draw legs and feet on the black bird with a black pastel. Using blue and green pastels, add an eye and lots of lines and patterns.

Pirate flags

1. To make the flags, fold several narrow rectangles of paper in half, with their short ends together. Crease the folds well.

2. With the fold at the top, draw an upside down 'V' at the bottom of each flag. Then, cut along the lines, keeping the layers together.

The glue stops the flags from sliding along the thread.

3. Draw skulls and bones, anchors, flags and palm trees on pieces of paper. Cut out the shapes and glue them onto the flags.

4. Open out the flags and spread glue along the folds. Fold the flags over a long piece of thread and press the glued parts together.

Dancing fairies

1. Draw the arms, head, eyes, mouth and body with a black pen. Add loop shapes for her skirt, then draw her legs and wings.

2. Fill in the skirt with a pink pencil. Then, draw pink circles on her cheeks and add a nose. Fill in her body with a purple pencil.

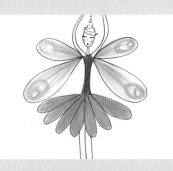

3. Draw two ovals inside the end of each wing. Draw some lines from the ovals to her body, then fill the wings with light shading.

4. For the fairy's ballet shoes, fill in the tips of her toes with a black pen. Then, add some crosses going up her legs for ribbons.

Cut-paper flowers

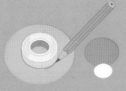

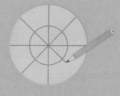

1. Draw around three round objects of different sizes on different shades of thick paper.

2. Cut out the circles. Lay the middle-sized object in the big circle and draw around it.

3. Draw a line across the big circle. Add a second line, crossing it. Then, draw two more lines, like this.

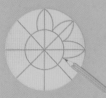

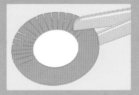

4. Draw petals from the edge of the big circle to the edge of the middle circle. Cut around the petals.

5. Glue the small circle onto the middle-sized circle. Then, make small cuts around the edge.

6. Glue the smaller circles onto the big one. Tape one end of a straw to the back of the flower.

7. Press a piece of poster tack onto the other end of the straw and press it into a jar.

8. Scrunch up pieces of tissue paper and push them into the jar, around the stalk.

9. Cut two pointed leaves from green paper. Then, glue them onto the stalk, like this.

Fingerprint bunnies

You could fingerprint a bird's head and body, then add little prints for wings and a tail.

Mix the paints on an old plate.

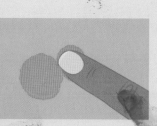

1. Make two blobs of bright pink paint by mixing red and white paints. Then, mix more white paint into one blob to make it paler pink.

2. Dip one of your fingers into the bright pink paint and fingerprint a body. Then, fingerprint a head on one side of the body.

Only press the top part of your finger onto the paper.

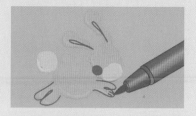

3. Use your little finger to fingerprint the legs. Then, dip the side of your little finger into the paint and print two long ears.

4. Using the paler paint, fingerprint a patch on the bunny's head, where the nose and mouth will be. Add a print for the tail, too.

5. When the paint is dry, draw a cheek using a pink felt-tip pen. Draw shapes inside the ears and around the legs. Add lines for claws.

6. Use a black felt-tip pen to add dots for eyes. Draw a round nose and add curves for a smiling mouth. Then, draw lines for whiskers.

Sequin card

1. Cut two squares of clear book covering film. Make them the same size. Then, carefully peel the backing paper off one of them.

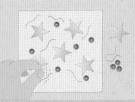

2. Lay the film on a table, sticky-side up. Press lots of sequins and little pieces of thread onto the film. Then, sprinkle on some glitter.

3. Peel the backing paper off the other piece of film. Carefully lay it on top of the decorated piece of film, with its sticky side facing down.

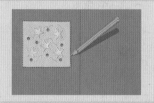

4. For the card, fold a piece of thick paper in half, then open it out. Lay the film on the left-hand side of the card and draw around it.

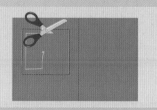

5. Make a hole in the middle of the square with a pencil, then push a scissor blade through it. Cut a 'window' smaller than the square.

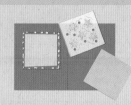

6. Spread glue around the 'window' and press on the decorated film. Then, cut a square of paper and glue it on top, to cover the film.

Painted flowerpots

Spotted pot

1. For a spotted pot, wash a terracotta flowerpot thoroughly. Leave it to dry out, then paint the outside with white acrylic paint.

2. Paint inside the top of the pot, too. Leave the paint to dry, then paint some light and dark purple circles on the pot.

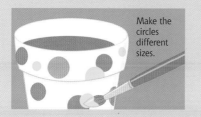

Make the circles different sizes.

3. When the purple circles are dry, paint yellow circles overlapping them. Leave the paint to dry, then put a pretty plant in the pot.

Flowery pot

1. For a flowery pot, wash a flowerpot and let it dry. Paint it a pale shade. Cut some circles and petal shapes from different shades of thin paper.

Use a glue stick.

2. Glue some of the petals onto the pot to make a flower. Then, glue a circle in the middle of the flower. Glue on more flowers.

The glue is clear when it dries.

3. Paint a thick layer of white glue all over the outside of the pot, including the flowers. When the glue is dry, put a pretty plant in the pot.

Printed owl

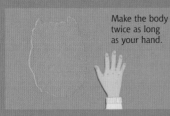

Make the body twice as long as your hand.

Rinse your spoon each time.

1. Rip a big oval body from brown paper. Then, rip a piece out of the top to leave two tufty ears. Glue the body onto blue paper.

2. Put three paper towels on some newspaper. Pour black, white and orange paint on top. Spread the paint out with a spoon.

The stalk of the apple should be at the top.

You could push a fork into the carrot to use as a handle.

3. Cut a small apple in half. Dip one half into the white paint. Press it down near the top of the owl's body, to print his face.

4. Cut the pointed end off a carrot. Then, cut the end in half. Dip one half into the white paint. Press it onto the body to print feathers.

5. Finger paint two big orange eyes. Let them dry. Then, finger paint the black middles. Add fingerprints for speckles on the owl's tummy.

6. Dip the clean half of the carrot tip into the orange paint. Press it onto the face to print a beak. Then, finger paint some orange claws.

Poppy collage

1. Tear some orange and red tissue paper into large pieces, to make petal shapes.

2. Mix some white glue with a few drops of water. Glue one of the petals onto a piece of paper.

3. Add more petals. Overlap the paper in some places. Make some more poppies.

4. Cut leaves and stems from green tissue paper. Then, glue them around the flowers.

5. Brush a layer of glue over the poppies. This will give them a slightly shiny appearance.

6. When the glue is completely dry, add details on the petals with a thin black felt-tip pen.

Shimmering shapes

Brush on more glue if you need to.

1. Use a pencil to draw a heart on a piece of tissue paper. Lay it on some plastic foodwrap, then brush white glue along the pencil line.

2. Press a length of thread onto the glue. At the top of the heart, make a loop with the thread and press the end into the glue.

3. Brush a thin layer of glue inside the heart. Then, cut some pieces of thread and press them into the glue, so that they overlap.

4. Brush another layer of glue over the top. Lightly sprinkle glitter over the shape and leave it until the glue has completely dried.

5. Carefully peel the tissue paper off the foodwrap and cut around the heart. Then, glue some sequins between the threads.

Flower garland

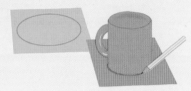

1. Lay a saucer on a piece of pale pink paper and draw around it. Then, draw around a mug on a piece of bright pink paper.

2. Draw around a bottle top on a piece of white paper. Then, cut out all the circles you have drawn and glue them together, like this.

3. For the petals, cut very thin triangles carefully into the biggest circle. Only cut as far as the edge of the bright pink circle.

4. Make more flowers, then cut a drinking straw into short pieces. Tape one piece of straw near the top of each flower, like this.

5. With the pieces of straw at the tops of the flowers, thread a long piece of ribbon through them all. Then, hang the flowers up.

Royal picture frame

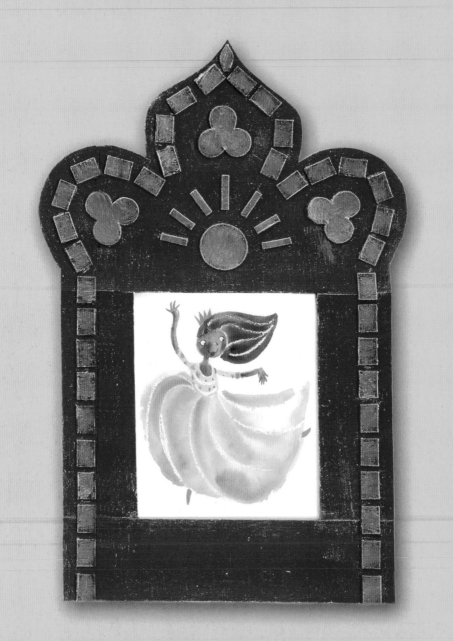

1. Place your picture in the middle of a rectangle of thick paper and draw around it. Put the picture to one side for later.

2. Make a hole in the middle of the rectangle with a ballpoint pen. Push scissors into the hole and cut around the pencil line.

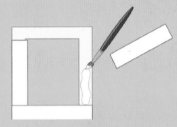

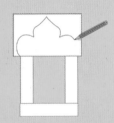

3. Cut three strips of thick cardboard for the bottom and sides of the frame. Then, glue them onto the paper frame.

4. Draw a pretty arch that fits onto the top of the frame, like this. Then, cut out the arch and glue it onto the frame.

5. Cut out cardboard shapes and glue them onto the frame. Paint the finished frame with purple paint, then let it dry.

6. Brush some gold paint over the purple paint, to make your frame look old. Then tape your picture onto the back.

Spooky painting

1. Dip a big paintbrush into dark pink paint. Then, paint across the top of a large piece of thick paper or cardboard.

2. Add a band of orange paint across the middle. Fill in the rest with yellow. Don't worry if the paint runs together.

3. Rinse your brush well. Then, blend the paint together by brushing across the paper where the different bands meet.

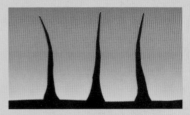

4. Paint a wiggly black line across the bottom of the paper. Fill in below it. Add some black lines for tree trunks, like this.

5. Add several black branches to the tree trunks. Add some even thinner twigs at the ends of some of the branches.

6. Paint some bats flying around the trees or hanging from branches. You could also add an owl.

Fingerprinted horse

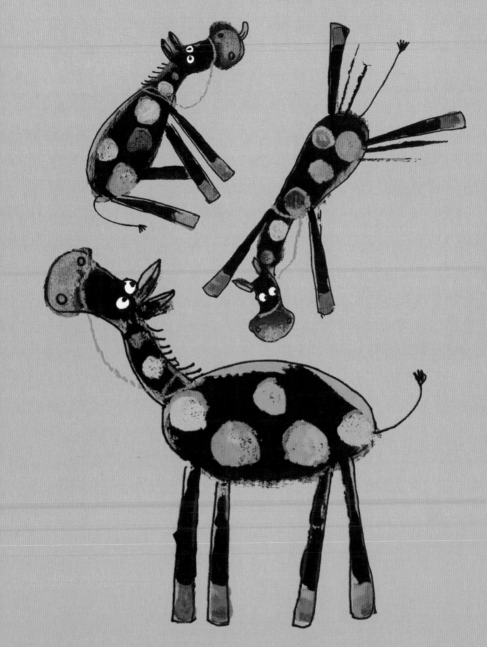

1. Dip your finger into black paint and fingerprint around and around for the body. Fingerprint the neck, head and ears, too.

2. Dip the edge of a piece of cardboard into black paint, then scrape it across the paper to print the legs. Add fingerprinted spots, too.

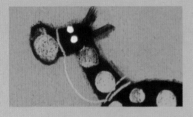

3. Print the eyes with white paint on the tip of your little finger. Draw the horse's reins with a blue chalk pastel.

4. Use a thin black felt-tip pen to outline the body, and draw the mane and tail. Outline the eyes and draw dots on them.

You could paint a horse sitting down, too.

5. For hooves, dip the end of a thin strip of cardboard into light brown paint. Scrape the cardboard across the bottom of the horse's legs.

49

Collage butterflies

 These are for the butterfly's wings.

1. On a thick piece of cardboard, draw two teardrops, one a little smaller than the other. Cut them out.

2. Draw around the big teardrop twice on a piece of patterned paper or material, to make two shapes.

3. Draw around the small teardrop twice on another piece of paper or material. Cut out all four shapes.

4. Glue the teardrops onto some thick paper, with the big shapes above the small ones, like this.

5. Cut out a shape for the body from thick material. Glue the body down the middle of the wings.

6. Using a thin paintbrush, brush stripes across the body with thick paint. Add eyes and feelers.

7. Glue two circles of material onto the ends of the feelers. Glue a sequin on top of each circle.

8. Glue two more circles onto the wings. Glue stars cut from shiny paper onto the wings, too.

51

Sparkly beads

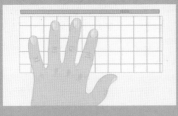

1. Cut a strip of book covering film as long as a thick drinking straw. Make the strip of film a little taller than your middle finger.

2. Peel the backing paper off the book covering film and lay it sticky-side up on a newspaper. Press the straw along one edge of the film.

Leave the top half empty.

3. Hold some tinsel over the strip of film. Then, snip along the tinsel, so that sparkly pieces fall onto the bottom half of the film.

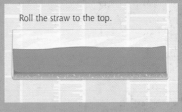

Roll the straw to the top.

4. Cut a strip of tissue paper, then lay it over the pieces of tinsel. Tightly roll the straw over the paper, tinsel and book film.

5. Cut the straw into bead-sized pieces. Tie one bead onto a long piece of thread and string on the rest of the beads to make a chain.

You could make shiny beads by rolling a straw in kitchen foil.

To make striped beads, lay pieces of gift ribbon on the book covering film.

Cut-and-stick castle

1. Tear a long strip of green paper for the grass. Glue it along the bottom of a big piece of paper.

Make the rectangles different sizes.

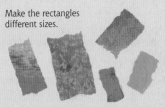

2. Rip some rectangles for towers from bright paper. You could use giftwrap or pages from old magazines.

3. Glue the biggest shape in the middle. Add other rectangles at the sides, overlapping each other.

4. Cut out some triangles for the roofs. Make sure that they are wider than the tops of the shapes for the towers.

5. Glue the roofs onto the tops of the towers. Then, cut out a door and glue it onto the castle.

6. Cut out window shapes from darker paper and glue them on. Add some windowsills, too.

Flower wall hanging

1. Lay a piece of plastic foodwrap on a magazine. Rip two shades of pink tissue paper into pieces.

2. Lay the pieces of tissue paper all over the foodwrap. Overlap them a little, like this, so there are no gaps.

3. Mix some white glue with water so that it is runny. Then, brush it all over the tissue paper.

4. Add two more layers of ripped tissue paper and glue. Then, sprinkle glitter on the top.

5. When the glue is dry, brush another layer of white glue over the glitter. Then, leave it to dry.

6. On another piece of plastic foodwrap, repeat steps 1-5, using yellow and orange tissue paper.

7. When it is dry, peel off the tissue paper. Cut out pink and orange flowers and small circles.

8. Glue pink circles onto the orange flowers and orange circles onto the pink flowers, like this.

9. Cut some pieces of thin ribbon. Then, tape the flowers onto the ribbons to make a wall hanging.

Tissue paper birds

1. Rip a rough shape for a bird's body from pink tissue paper. Then, rip two shapes for the wings and another for the tail.

Brush the glue to the edge.

2. Gently brush white glue on the back of the body. Press it onto a piece of white paper, then glue on the wings and tail.

3. Rip a shape for another bird's body and two shapes for wings from blue tissue paper. Then, glue them onto the paper, too.

4. Rip lots of small pieces from pink tissue paper. Glue them in the spaces around the birds, then leave the glue to dry.

5. Using a black felt-tip pen, draw outlines for the birds' bodies. You don't need to follow the edges of the tissue paper too closely.

6. Draw the birds' tails, wings, legs and beaks. Add eyes and feathers on their heads. Draw hearts on the small pieces of tissue paper.

Dinosaur painting

1. Use a pencil to draw a dinosaur's nose, then add a line for the bottom jaw. Add a frill at the back of the head, then draw eyes and eyebrows.

2. Draw a fat body shape and a pointed tail. Then, add three short legs below the body – the fourth leg is hidden from view.

3. Brush clean water over your drawing. Then, dab watery paint onto the water so that it runs. Dab more paint on the tummy and tail.

4. When the paint is dry, draw over the pencil lines with a black felt-tip pen. Add spots on the frill and toenails on the feet.

5. Using a red chalk pastel, draw lots of lines on the dinosaur's body, tail and legs. Then, add a balloon and gift with a pencil.

6. Fill in the balloon and gift with watery paints. When they are dry, outline them with a black pen. Then, add more dinosaurs.

Fairy door sign

Poppy's Room

Keep this piece for later.

1. Using a pencil, draw around a small plate on a piece of paper. Then, cut out the circle.

2. Fold the circle in half, then in half again. Open it out, then cut out one quarter, like this.

3. Draw two wings touching the folds. Cut around the wings and along the folds, like this.

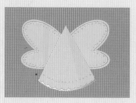

Decorate the arms.

4. Decorate the fairy. Push the wings together, to curve the body. Glue them onto thick paper.

5. Draw and cut out a face and hair, then glue them together. Draw arms on the spare quarter circle.

6. Cut out the arms, then cut out hands and glue them on. Glue the arms and head onto the body.

Make one end rounded.

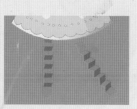

7. For the fairy's legs, cut two long strips of paper. Then, fold each strip lots of times, to make zigzags.

8. Glue the flat ends of the zigzag legs under the body. Make sure the rounded ends are at the bottom.

9. Cut a heart shape around the fairy and write your name. Then, press on lots of shiny stickers.

Tissue flowers

You could use these ideas to
decorate an Easter card.

1. Use a pink pencil to draw a stalk with two leaves. Then, draw a big oval at the top with lots of small petals around it.

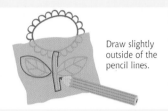

Draw slightly outside of the pencil lines.

2. Lay some green tissue paper over the stalk and draw around it. Then, draw around the leaves in the same way. Cut them out.

3. Lay tissue paper over the oval. Draw around it and cut it out. Then, draw and cut out the petals from yellow paper.

4. Brush white glue over the pencil stalk and lay the tissue paper stalk on top. Then, brush some more glue over the top.

5. Then, glue on the leaves, petals and oval over the pencil lines. Cut out some little circles of tissue paper and glue them in the middle of the flower.

The petals will overlap.

To make a tulip, draw a stalk and leaves. Then, draw a flower shape, like this. Glue on a tissue paper stalk, leaves and three big petals.

Pirate door sign

The lid of a spice jar is ideal.

1. Lay a roll of sticky tape near the top of a long piece of thick white paper. Then, draw around the sticky tape with a pencil.

2. Draw two lines from the circle to the bottom of the paper. Lay the lid of a small jar on the circle and draw around it.

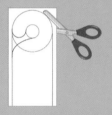

3. Draw two curving lines from the small circle, like this. Then, cut out the door sign shape, following the pencil lines.

4. Draw a pirate's head halfway down the main part of the door sign. Add a headscarf, hair and ears, then draw his face.

5. Draw his body, arms and sword, then draw over all the lines with a black felt-tip pen. Then, fill in the picture with other pens.

6. Draw stripes across the sign and fill them in with a red pen. Then, write your name or a message on the pirate's sword.

Elephant chain

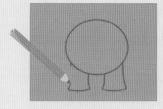

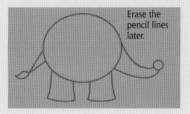

Erase the pencil lines later.

1. Using a pencil, lightly draw an oval for an elephant's body on thick paper. Draw two leg shapes below the body, too.

2. Draw a trunk with a circle at the end. Then, draw a tail shape with a tassel at the end. Cut out the elephant.

They should all face the same way.

3. Draw around the elephant on different shades of paper, then cut out the elephants. Draw black eyes and ears.

4. Cut out shapes for the elephants' tusks and toenails from shiny paper or foil. Then, glue them onto the elephants.

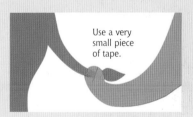

Use a very small piece of tape.

5. Decorate the elephants by cutting out different shapes and gluing them on. Use sequins, beads, pens and glitter glue, too.

6. Make a small cut into each elephant's trunk. Slot the thin part of another elephant's tail into the slit. Secure them all with tape.

Cartoon faces

1. Paint an oval shape for the face with watery paint. Paint a body below the face, then add some orange hair.

2. When the paint is completely dry, draw around the face with a thin black pen. Then, add a face and two ears.

3. Use the pen to draw a few lines on the hair. Use curly, wavy or straight lines for different kinds of hair.

4. Draw a scarf below the face. Then, draw curved lines for shoulders and two short lines for arms.

You could draw lots of people, to make a crowd.

Big flower prints

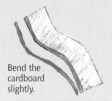

1. For a primrose, spread yellow paint onto newspaper. Cut a pear in half. Press it into the paint.

2. Print a pear shape onto some paper for a petal. Put a bottle top at the pointed end of the shape.

3. Print more petals around the bottle top. Dip the pear in the paint each time you do a print.

This will make a leaf shape.

Bend the cardboard slightly.

4. Lift off the bottle top. Dip a fingertip into green paint and print dots in the middle of the petals.

5. Carefully cut a little potato in half. Dip it in green paint. Press it onto the paper around the flower.

6. For a bluebell stalk, make prints with the edge of a long piece of cardboard dipped in green paint.

Use the other half of the potato.

7. Dip a smaller piece of cardboard into the green paint. Do several prints along the stalk.

8. Cut the spare half of the potato in half. Use a knife to cut a zigzag carefully along the straight edge.

9. Dip the potato half into light blue paint and print a bluebell flower on the end of each stalk.

Hearts card

1. Spread white glue on a strip of paper. Then, sprinkle glitter over the wet glue and leave it to dry.

2. Cut a vase shape and a heart from two shades of bright paper. Glue the heart onto the vase.

3. Cut three small paper hearts and three bigger ones. Glue the small hearts onto the big ones.

Put your thumb here.

4. Cut the glittery paper into three strips. Then, glue the hearts onto the ends of the strips.

5. Cut three pieces of gift ribbon. Tape them to the back of the vase. Then, tape on the strips, too.

6. To curl a ribbon, hold it against closed scissors, then pull it across them, like this. Curl all the ribbons.

You could decorate a card with flowers instead of hearts.

7. Fold a piece of thick paper to make a card. Glue on the vase, then bend the glittery strips over.

8. Draw lots of hearts on shiny paper. Cut them out and glue them on. Glue on sequins, too.

Paper caterpillar

Fold

You don't need this piece.

1. Fold a piece of bright paper in half, with the long sides together. Then, cut along the fold.

2. Sponge a different shade of bright paint on each side of one of the pieces of paper. Let the paint dry.

3. Fold the paper in half, then in half again. Open it out and cut along the folds to make four strips.

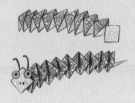

Crease here.

Fold this strip down.

4. Dab some glue at the end of one strip. Then, press on the end of another strip, like this.

5. Fold the left strip over and crease it. Then, fold the other strip down over the top of it.

6. Keep folding one strip neatly over the other one, until you have a folded zigzag of paper.

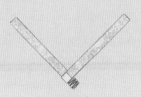

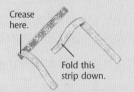

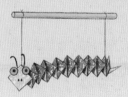

7. When you get to the end of the strips, glue on the spare strips and fold them to the end.

8. Glue down the ends, then glue on eyes and a tail. Add short feelers cut from a pipe cleaner.

9. Tape a piece of thread behind the head and the tail. Then, tie the ends of the thread onto a straw.

Springtime crown

Make sure the paper fits around your head.

1. Draw a zigzag on a long wide strip of thick green paper, leaving a space at each end. Cut it out.

2. For the flower stalks, cut lots of strips of green paper, taller than the height of the crown.

3. Draw flowers with five petals on yellow or orange paper, then draw smaller flowers with square ends.

4. Cut the flowers out. Glue the small ones onto the big ones, like this. Bend the little petals up.

5. Tape a stalk to the back of each flower. Tape the stalks in between the zigzags on the crown.

6. For bees, cut out bodies and wings from paper. Draw eyes and stripes on the bodies. Glue on the wings.

7. Cut out some long thin stalks from green paper. Tape a stalk onto the back of each bee.

8. Tape the bees in between the flowers. Cut out flowers from white paper. Glue on yellow middles.

9. Glue the flowers onto the crown. Bend the crown around your head and tape it together to secure it.

Sparkly chains

1. Dab lots of small blobs of white glue all over a large piece of bright paper. Then, sprinkle glitter all over the wet glue, like this.

2. When the glue is dry, tip the extra glitter onto an old newspaper. Then, use the glitter to decorate another piece of bright paper.

Make sure that the glitter is on the outside.

3. Leave the glue to dry. Then, use scissors to cut both pieces of paper into lots of strips. Try to make all the strips the same width.

4. Bend one of the strips into a loop. Secure the join with a piece of sticky tape. Then, thread another strip through the loop and tape it.

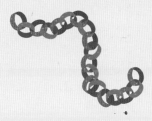

5. Thread another strip through the loop and tape it in place. Continue until you have used all the strips, then hang up the chain.

To make a chain like this one, sprinkle several pieces of paper with different shades of glitter. You could use glitter glue, too.

Butterfly card

1. Pour some blue paint onto an old plate and mix it with water to make it runny. Then, use a small brush to paint butterfly wings, like this.

2. Wash your brush. Then, while the blue paint is wet, dab small dots of green paint onto it. The green paint will spread a little.

3. Leave the paint to dry. Then, paint a dark blue body in the middle of the wings. Add thin feelers to the top of the body.

4. Paint lots more butterflies. Try painting orange wings with red bodies etc. Then, leave the paint to dry.

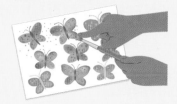

5. Make your painting into a card by folding a sheet of thick paper in half. Cut around the butterflies and glue them onto the card.

6. For a splattered effect, dip a dry brush into some runny paint. Hold the brush over the card and pull a finger quickly over the bristles.

Royal crowns

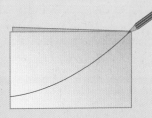

1. Cut a rectangle of thick paper that is long enough to fit around your head, with a little overlap. Then, fold it in half.

2. Using a pencil, draw a curved line across the paper. The pencil line should go to the top corner of the folded edge, like this.

Only cut halfway into the paper.

3. Draw curly shapes below the first pencil line, like this. Add some against the fold, too. Then, carefully cut along the curly lines.

4. Unfold the paper. Make a cut going down into it, a little way from one end. Then, make a second cut going up into the other end.

You could make a tiara like this one by drawing slanting lines in step 3.

5. Decorate the tiara with lots of sequins and beads, and gold and silver pens. Then, slot the tiara together with its ends on the inside.

Scratched patterns

1. Use different oil pastels to draw lots of patches on a piece of white paper. Make sure that the patches join together, like this.

2. Mix a little water with some thick black paint. Use acrylic paint if you have it. Cover the oil pastel patches completely with the paint.

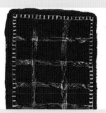

3. Leave the paint until it is almost dry. Then, use a screwdriver to gently scratch lines in the paint, to reveal the oil pastels underneath.

4. Scratch several more lines down the paint. Then, scratch lines across it to make a large grid. Scratch a border around the edge, too.

5. Scratch a simple outline of a bird in part of the grid. Then, add some curved lines for feathers, a wing, an eye and a beak.

6. If you make a mistake, paint over it with some black paint. Let the paint dry a little before you scratch into it again.

Fairy wings

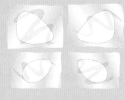

1. Draw two big and two smaller wings on paper. Cut them out, then lay plastic foodwrap over them.

2. Rip up white tissue paper. Overlap lots of pieces on the plastic, covering the wings and their edges.

3. Mix white glue with water to make it runny. Then, brush it over the pieces of tissue paper.

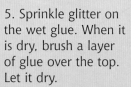

4. Add a layer of ripped pieces of pink tissue paper and glue. Then, add two more white layers.

5. Sprinkle glitter on the wet glue. When it is dry, brush a layer of glue over the top. Let it dry.

6. Peel off the tissue paper. Lay the paper wings on top, draw around them and cut out the shapes.

Use a ballpoint pen.

7. Glue the top parts of the wings onto the bottom parts. Decorate the wings with sequins.

8. Make four holes in a small cardboard rectangle. Thread two long ribbons through the holes.

9. Glue the rectangle onto the back of the wings, with the ribbons sticking out. Let the glue dry.

Egg toppers

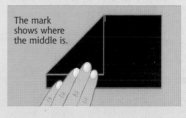

The mark shows where the middle is.

1. For a pirate hat, cut a piece of paper 15 x 10cm (6 x 4in). Fold it in half so that the short sides are together and the fold is at the top.

2. Bend the paper in half and pinch the corner to make a mark. Then, unfold the paper and fold the corners into the middle, like this.

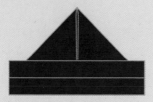

You only need one half for the hat.

3. Fold up the top layer of paper at the bottom of the hat. Then, turn the hat over and fold the paper on that side up in the same way.

4. For a pointed hat, lay a small plate on a piece of paper. Draw around it. Cut out the circle and fold it in half. Then, cut along the fold.

Make all the triangles the same size.

5. Bend the paper around so that the corners overlap and make a cone. Then, secure the edges with small pieces of sticky tape.

6. For a crown, cut a paper strip that will fit around an egg. Cut out triangles along the top. Bend the paper around and tape the ends.

Flower cards

1. Cut a rectangle of thin cardboard. Then, fold it in half to make a card. Rip a square of tissue paper and glue it onto the front.

2. Open the card and lay it on a folded paper towel. Carefully, push a needle all around the edges of the card to make lots of little holes.

3. Glue a square of patterned material about the size of the card onto a piece of paper. Draw a flower on the material and cut it out.

4. Draw another slightly larger flower on a plain piece of material and cut it out. Thread a needle. Tie a knot near the end of the thread.

5. Push the needle through the middle of the large flower, then push it through the small one. Push a sequin and a bead onto the needle.

Sew through the loop to secure the thread.

6. Sew back through the sequin and flowers. Tie a loop in the thread and sew through it. Cut off any hanging ends. Glue the flower to the card.

Marzipan toadstools

To make 8 toadstools, you will need:
a block of 'white' marzipan*
red food dye

The toadstools need to be stored in
an airtight container and eaten
within three weeks.

*Marzipan contains ground nuts, so don't give
the toadstools to anyone who is allergic to nuts.

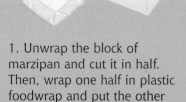

1. Unwrap the block of marzipan and cut it in half. Then, wrap one half in plastic foodwrap and put the other half in a small bowl.

2. Wash your hands, then add three drops of red food dye to the bowl and mix it in with your fingers. Then, break the marzipan into eight pieces.

Wash your hands again.

3. Roll each piece into a ball, then squash them to make toadstool shapes. Press your thumb into the bottom to make a hollow, like this.

4. Unwrap the other half of the marzipan. To make spots, break off a third of the marzipan and roll it into lots of little balls.

5. Gently press several of the little balls onto each toadstool. Then, break the remaining piece of marzipan into eight pieces.

6. Roll each piece between your fingers to make a thick stalk. Then, press a red top onto each stalk to complete the toadstool.

Sparkly frame

1. Lay the picture you want to frame on a piece of thick paper. Then, use a pencil to draw lightly around the picture, like this.

2. Draw another rectangle inside the first one. Then, push a sharp pencil through the middle of the smaller rectangle, to make a hole.

3. Push one scissor blade through the hole. Then, cut around the edge of the smaller rectangle to make a 'window' in the frame.

4. Cut strips of paper that are as wide as the frame. Then, cut the strips into squares and glue them around the frame, like this.

5. To make your frame sparkly, brush on spots of white glue and sprinkle them with glitter. Let the glue dry. Then, press on shiny stickers, too.

6. When the glue is dry, turn the frame over. Lay the picture face down and tape it in place. Then, tape on a loop of thread for hanging.

Fingerprint dinosaurs

Rub your
finger around
for the body.

1. Spread green paint on an
old plate, then dip a finger into
it. Fingerprint some blobs on
paper for a body and a head.

2. Dip your finger into the
paint again and fingerprint two
legs. Use a paintbrush to paint
a long neck and a pointed tail.

3. Let the paint dry. Fingerprint
dark green spines along the
dinosaur's back, then fingerprint
blue spots on the body.

4. Paint some white eyes.
When the paint is dry, outline
them with a pen. Then, outline
the head and add nostrils.

You could
draw stripes
instead of spots
on a dinosaur.

5. Draw around the body and
legs, going straight across the
spines on the back, not around
them. Add toenails, too.

Hearts giftwrap

1. To make a stencil, fold a piece of thick paper in half. Draw half a heart against the fold, then cut along the line. Keep both pieces of paper.

2. Mix some red paint with white glue on an old plate. Then, spread the paint out on the plate a little with the back of a spoon.

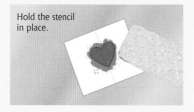

Hold the stencil in place.

Don't move the stencil.

3. Lay the stencil on a large piece of thin paper. Dab a sponge into the paint. Then dab it over the heart, until the shape is filled with paint.

4. Before the paint has had a chance to dry, sprinkle red glitter all over the heart. Gently press the glitter on with your fingers.

5. Move the stencil and print lots more hearts, all over the paper. Sprinkle glitter on the hearts, then leave the paint to dry completely.

For a tag, lay the heart that you cut out from the stencil in step 1 on some folded paper. Dab paint over the tag, then sprinkle it with glitter.

Leafy picture

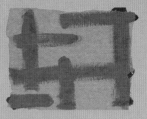

1. Use dark paint and a thick paintbrush to paint some horizontal and vertical lines on your paper.

2. When the paint has dried completely, cut a piece of tissue paper to cover the lines, and glue it on top.

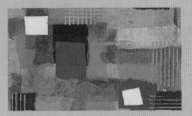

3. Rip some squares and rectangles from different shades of tissue paper and glue them on.

4. Press a small square of corrugated cardboard into some paint. Print it several times on the tissue paper.

5. Cut out leaves from a picture in a magazine, or cut some leaf shapes from paper. Then, glue them on.

6. Add shapes cut from a magazine picture of grass. Add lines with a black pen. Then, outline the leaves.

Speckled butterflies

1. Paint all over a sheet of thick white paper with watery paint. Then, sprinkle grains of salt onto the paint and leave it to dry.

2. When the paint is completely dry, brush off the salt. Then, fold the paper in half and glue it together with the paint on the outside.

The fold needs to be on this side.

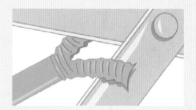

3. Fold the paper in half again. Draw two butterfly wings on it, then cut around the wings, through all the layers of paper.

4. For each butterfly, cut the end off a drinking straw, just above the bumpy part. To make feelers, cut down into the bumpy part.

Snip here.

Make sure that the bead is wider than the straw.

5. Bend the feelers out, then open the wings. Lay the straw in the fold in the middle of the butterfly, then snip off the bottom end of the straw.

6. Push a piece of ribbon through a bead. Tie a knot in the ribbon and push it through the straw. Glue the straw onto the wings.

Decorated eggs

You don't need the yolk and egg white.

Match the cracked edges if you can.

1. Crack an egg sharply on the rim of a mug. Then, carefully break the egg in half over the mug.

2. Wash the eggshells and leave them to dry completely. Brush white glue along the cracked edge of one half.

3. Fit the other half on top. Brush glue around the crack to seal it. Put it in an egg carton to dry.

4. Rip some tissue paper into small pieces. Then, brush the top half of the egg with white glue.

5. Press the pieces of paper onto the wet glue. Add more glue and paper until the top is covered.

6. When the glue is dry, cover the bottom half with tissue paper in the same way. Leave it to dry.

Decorate one side first, then let it dry.

Make up patterns of your own or use the ideas below.

7. Mix some paint with a little white glue. Paint one half of the egg. When it is dry, paint the rest.

8. When the paint is dry, mix other paints with glue. Decorate your egg with flowers and spots.

Tissue paper owl

Make the body twice as long as the head.

1. Draw a slanted oval for the owl's body, and another oval for its head. Add wing shapes and clawed feet.

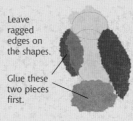

Leave ragged edges on the shapes.

Glue these two pieces first.

2. Using tissue paper, tear a shape for the head and body, two wings and a tree stump. Glue them all on.

3. With a black felt-tip pen, draw the beak, tufts and eyes. Fill them in. Add lines between the tufts, too.

4. Using felt-tip pens, draw zigzag lines around the eyes. Add slanted lines and a nostril on the beak.

5. Draw lots of curved lines for downy breast feathers. Outline the feet and draw curved dashes on them.

Start at the top of the wings and work down.

6. Use a thick felt-tip pen to fill the wings with long feathers. Add lines in the feathers and fill in their tips.

Octopus mobile

The slits should reach halfway.

1. Draw a four-legged octopus on cardboard. Cut it out, then draw around it on another piece of cardboard.

2. Cut out the other octopus. Hold them together, with one upside down. Cut a slit into both bodies.

3. Lay the bodies on a newspaper. Paint both sides with orange paint, then let the paint dry.

Splatter paint on both sides.

4. Dip a dry brush into blue paint. Then, flick the bristles to splatter paint over the bodies. Leave it to dry.

5. Draw lots of fish to hang from the mobile on another piece of cardboard. Cut out the shapes.

6. Cut eight long pieces of thread. Tape the fish onto the ends of the threads with sticky tape.

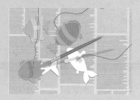

7. Paint both sides of the fish, then let the paint dry completely. Add faces with a black felt-tip pen.

8. Tape a thread onto each leg. Paint blue rings at the bottom for suckers. Then, let the paint dry.

9. Slot the slit of one body into the other. Draw a face. Open the mobile and add a thread for hanging.

Printed collage card

1. Cut a rectangle from a piece of thick paper and fold it in half. Cut a smaller one from thick cardboard.

2. Tape the end of a piece of string to one end of the cardboard. Wind the string around and around.

3. Continue until you get to the end. Then, cut the string and tape it onto the cardboard, like this.

4. Paint the string with thick yellow paint. Then, press it onto the folded card, to print yellow lines.

5. Print more lines, adding more paint as you go, until the card is covered with lots of yellow lines.

6. Cut a smaller square from yellow paper, and an even smaller one from light green paper.

7. Wrap some string around another piece of cardboard. Print green lines onto the green square.

8. When the paint has dried, glue the yellow square to the front of the card. Glue the green square on top.

9. Cut out a white paper flower and a yellow middle. Glue them onto the middle of the card.

Party mask

1. Cut long strips from pink and blue tissue paper. Make them the width of two fingers.

2. Glue the blue strips across some cardboard. Glue the pink strips the other way.

3. Turn over the cardboard. Lay a pair of sunglasses on it and draw around them.

4. Draw shapes where your eyes will be. Add a mask shape around the outline. Cut it out.

5. Press a sharp pencil point, then a scissor blade into the eyeholes. Cut them out.

6. Turn the mask over. Draw lines of glitter glue along the edges of the tissue paper strips.

Don't cover the bumpy part.

Tape over the bumpy part to make it stronger.

7. Cut a strip of shiny paper, big enough to cover a straw. Spread glue on the back of it.

8. Lay the long end of a bendable straw at the edge of the paper. Roll the straw in the paper.

9. Trim the ends of the paper. Bend the straw. Then, tape the top part to the back of the mask.

Glittery boxes

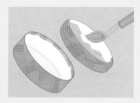

1. Mix some white glue with a little water. Then, cut bright tissue paper into small pieces.

2. Brush a box and lid with glue. Press pieces of tissue paper onto the wet glue, overlapping them.

3. Brush on another layer of glue and add more tissue paper. Add more layers, then let the glue dry.

4. To make 'sequins', punch lots of holes in some shiny paper. Then, empty the hole puncher onto a plate.

5. Using the tip of a paintbrush, dab blobs of glue around the edge of the lid. Press on the sequins.

6. Brush a spiral of glue on the lid, then sprinkle glitter over it. When it is dry, shake off any excess glitter.

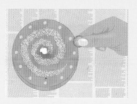

Try adding different glitter shapes, such as stars, onto the lid.

7. For a 'gem', dip a piece of tissue paper into the glue. Roll it into a ball, then roll it in some glitter.

8. Let the gem dry. Then, dab a blob of glue in the middle of the spiral and press on the gem.

Painted buildings

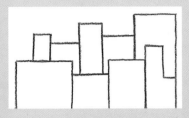

1. Use a pencil to draw several large rectangles on a piece of paper. Make the shapes different sizes.

2. Add domes to some of the rectangles. Make the domes different sizes and shapes like this, too.

3. Add lots of different shapes of windows, doorways, columns and arches to the buildings. Add some trees, too.

4. Use watery paints or inks to fill in the buildings. Leave a gap between each part, but don't fill in the domes.

5. When the paint or ink is completely dry, fill in the domes with a gold felt-tip pen or gold paint.

6. Draw around some of the windows and add patterns to the buildings, using a gold pen, too.

Princess hat

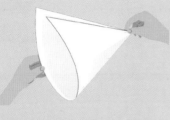

1. Draw half a circle on a large sheet of thick paper and cut it out. Bend the paper around and pinch the middle of the straight edge.

2. Wrap·the curved edge of the half circle around your head. Ask someone to slide one edge over the other until the cone fits neatly.

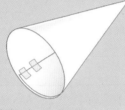

3. While the cone is on your head, ask someone to tape it together for you. Tape it on the outside, and then on the inside, too.

Overlap the pieces of tissue paper as you glue them on.

4. Rip different shades of tissue paper into small pieces. Brush glue over one patch of the cone at a time and press the pieces onto it.

5. Cover the whole cone in the same way. Then, cut several long strips of tissue paper or crêpe paper and tape them to the top.

6. Cut two hearts from shiny paper. Then, glue them onto the top of the cone, to hide the tape. Decorate your hat with sequins and stickers.

Mermaid chain

1. Fold a rectangle of paper in half, with its short sides together. Fold it in half again.

2. Draw a mermaid with her arms out, so her hands almost touch the edges of the paper.

3. Draw the tail curving to one side, making the tips of the tail close to the edge of the paper.

 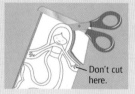

Don't cut here.

Tail folds

4. Draw a line around the mermaid that touches the edges of the paper by the hands and tail.

5. Cut along the line above the mermaid's arms and head. Be careful not to cut around her hands.

6. Cut along the lines around the arms and tail. Don't cut the folds by the mermaid's tail and hands.

7. Unfold the paper. Draw mermaids in the other shapes and decorate them all with felt-tip pens.

8. Using a shiny pen, draw scales on the tails and patterns on the tops. Add dots of glitter glue, too.

Marzipan rabbits

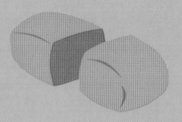

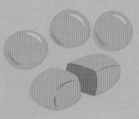

1. Put a block of marzipan into a mixing bowl. Add a drop of red food dye to make it pink. Cut the marzipan in half. Wash your hands.

2. With one half, roll the marzipan into three balls, for the rabbits' bodies. Then, cut the remaining piece of marzipan in half.

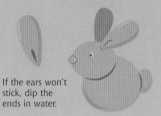

If the ears won't stick, dip the ends in water.

3. From one half, roll three smaller balls, for the heads. Then, make six ears, three tails and three noses from the other half.

4. Pinch each ear to make a fold. Press ears, a head, nose and tail onto each body. Then, press in eyes with a toothpick.

Press the head onto the body higher up, or lower down, to make rabbits in different positions.

To make carrots, roll out pieces of marzipan mixed with orange food dye.

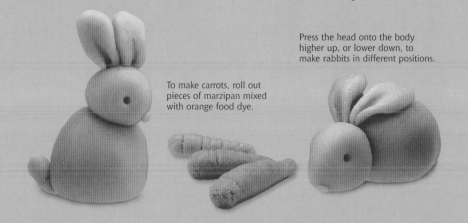

Mermaid bookmark

1. Fold a piece of foil in half. Then, spread a thin layer of white glue on the inside and press the foil together. Leave the glue to dry.

2. Put the foil on a pile of newspapers. Pressing hard with a ballpoint pen, draw a crown and a mermaid's tail. Then, cut out the shapes.

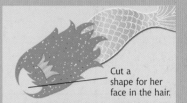

Cut a shape for her face in the hair.

3. Lay the crown on the sticky side of some book covering film. Sprinkle a little glitter around it, then lay tissue paper over the top.

4. Draw a wavy shape for the hair on the tissue paper. Cut out the hair and glue it onto the bumpy side of the tail, like this.

You could draw a fan-shaped or bumpy tail.

5. Glue the tail and the hair onto a piece of paper. Draw the mermaid's face and arms on the paper, then cut around the shapes.

Striped card

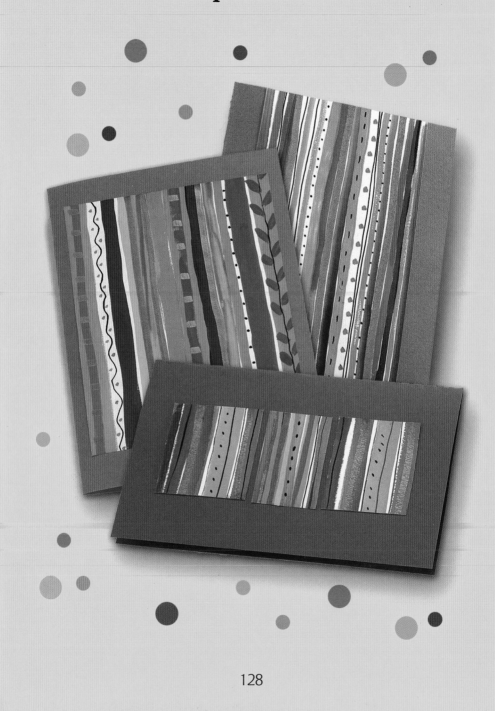

1. Using orange paint, paint a thick line down a piece of white paper. Add two thinner lines, one on each side of the thick line.

2. Paint a thick green line near the orange line, leaving a little gap. Add two thinner lines near one of the other orange lines.

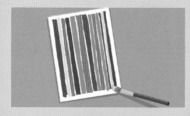

3. Paint blue, pink and yellow lines in the spaces, so that you fill the paper, like this. Then, leave the paint to dry.

4. Using a black felt-tip pen, draw dots on some of the stripes. Then, draw some wiggly lines on some of the other stripes.

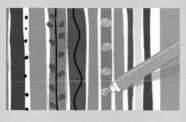

5. Paint pink blobs on one of the orange stripes. Then, when the paint is dry, use a gold pen to add more spots, dots and lines.

6. Fold a piece of thick paper to make a card. Cut around the striped painting so that it fits onto the card. Then, glue it on.

Sea horse pencil top

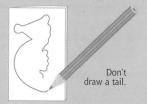

Don't draw a tail.

This will be the tail.

1. Fold a piece of thick paper in half. Draw a sea horse's body, like this. Then, cut out the shape, through both layers of paper.

2. Bend a pipe cleaner into a curved shape that follows the sea horse's body. Lay it on the sea horse and tape it in place.

Squeeze the edges until the glue dries.

3. Spread white glue over the paper and the pipe cleaner. Press the other sea horse on top and squeeze the edges together.

4. When the glue is dry, paint both sides of the body. Paint along the edges of the body, then paint the pipe cleaner, too.

5. When the paint is dry, paint patterns and an eye on each side of the sea horse. Then, wind the tail around the end of a pencil.

Curl the tail into a spiral for a sea horse charm.

Fairy tiara

Lay the foil shiny side down.

Press down hard.

1. Cut a wide strip of kitchen foil, longer than a pipe cleaner. Then, lay the pipe cleaner on top.

2. Squeeze the foil around the pipe cleaner. Roll it into a thin band, then roll it on a flat surface.

3. Cut five thin strips of foil, half the length of the band. Squeeze them into sticks and roll them.

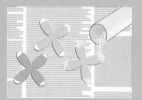

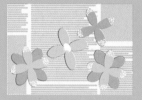

4. Cut three flowers with four petals. Dab white glue on the tips of the petals and sprinkle glitter on them.

5. Cut out three larger flowers. Dab glue in the middle of them and press on the glittery flowers.

6. Curl one end of each foil stick into a spiral. Glue one spiral onto the middle of each flower.

Gently bend the sticks to make them wiggly.

7. Lay the flowers in a row, glittery side down. Lay the band halfway up the stems, like this.

8. To attach the flowers, bend the bottom of the stems up. Then, twist them around the band.

9. Twist the other foil sticks onto the band. Glue on sequins, then bend the band into a curve.

Ink pen cars

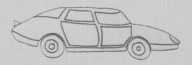

1. Draw an outline of a car with a pencil. You could use pictures from books, magazines or the internet for reference.

2. Draw the windows, doors, wheels and hubcaps. Then, add the headlights and rear lights, then the rear bumper.

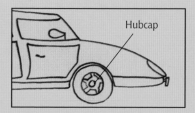

Hubcap

3. Using an ink pen, a dip pen or a black felt-tip pen, go over the pencil lines. Then, erase the pencil lines when the ink is dry.

4. Draw handles on the doors and add a bumper on the front of the car. Add a mirror, then draw shapes on the hubcaps.

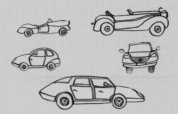

5. Draw lots more cars from different views. Do some from the side, some front-on and some from the back.

6. When the ink is completely dry, use chalk pastels or felt-tip pens to fill in different parts on each of the cars.

Painted parrot

1. Using a pencil, draw a shape for the parrot's head and body on a large piece of paper.

Leave room for the tail.

2. Draw an eye and a beak. Add some feathers on the head. Then, draw a branch and feet.

Leave the eye white.

3. Fill in the beak and feet with yellow paint. Let the paint dry. Then, fill in the rest with red paint.

4. Paint a red tail, then leave it to dry. Add yellow feathers on top, then add green feathers.

Use your right hand.

5. On an old plate, spread red, yellow, green and blue paint in stripes. Press one hand into the paint.

Print this wing first.

6. Turn the paper upside down. Then, print a wing onto the body with your hand, like this.

7. Turn the plate so that the red paint is on the right. Print the other wing with your left hand.

8. Paint a black dot on the eye and leave it to dry. Then, add a branch with thick, brown paint.

You can decorate the branch with leaves and flowers.

Shiny rosettes

The circles are for the back of the rosette.

1. Draw five petal shapes and a circle on a piece of thin cardboard. Cut them out. Then, cut five slightly larger petals and a circle from foil.

2. Glue each cardboard petal onto a foil petal, then fold the edges over, like this. Cover the circle, too. Then, bend each petal to make a curve.

3. Roll one end of a curved petal around a pencil, like this, to make it curl up. Then, do the same to the rest of the petals.

4. Dab a blob of white glue onto the middle of the silver · circle. Then, with the foil side facing up, press the petals into the glue, to make a flower.

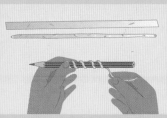

5. For tendrils, cut three strips of foil and roll them to make thin sticks. Wind the foil sticks around a pencil to make coils, like this.

6. Tape the coiled tendrils to the back of the rosette. Then, glue a small circle of purple paper onto the middle of the rosette.

Crayon chicks

1. Use an orange crayon to draw a circle on a piece of paper. This will be the body.

2. Fill in the circle with a yellow crayon. Then, draw an orange beak on one side.

3. Draw an eye near the beak. Add a wing shape using an orange crayon.

4. Draw lots of orange lines for a tail at the back of the chick. Add two brown legs.

This chick has spiky feathers on its head.

For a flying chick, draw the wings pointed up.

Printed ghosts

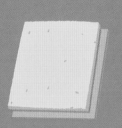

1. Glue a sponge cloth onto a piece of thin cardboard. This makes it less messy and easier to hold when you start printing with the sponge.

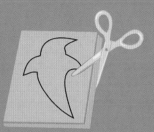

2. Use a pencil to draw the outline of a ghost on the cardboard. Then, cut around the ghost, through the cardboard and the sponge.

3. Brush orange and yellow paint over a large piece of white paper. While it dries, draw a castle on blue paper. Cut it out and glue it on.

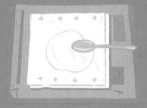

4. Lay some paper towels on an old newspaper. Then, spread white paint on the paper towels using the back of an old spoon.

5. Dip the sponge in the paint, then press it onto the castle. Rub the back slightly, then lift off the sponge. Print another ghost in the same way.

6. Follow steps 1-2 to make other ghosts and print them on the castle, too. When the paint is dry, add faces with a black felt-tip pen.

Frosted flowers

Keep the paper folded.

1. Fold a piece of tissue paper in half. Lay a mug on it and draw around it. Then, cut out the circle.

2. Lay the two circles on a newspaper. Dab white glue around their edges, then sprinkle it with glitter.

3. When the glue is dry, push one end of a sparkly pipe cleaner through both circles, to make a stem.

4. Slide the circles a little way down the stem. Pinch the tissue paper and twist it around the stem.

5. Secure the tissue paper to the stem with a piece of sticky tape. Open out the petals a little.

6. For a leaf, fold another piece of tissue paper in half. Draw a leaf shape, then cut it out.

7. Cut a pipe cleaner in half. Spread glue over one leaf. Then, press one end of the pipe cleaner onto it.

8. Press the other leaf on top. Spread glue over the leaf, then sprinkle the glue with lots of glitter.

9. When the glue is dry, lay the leaf stem next to the flower stem. Twist the pipe cleaners together.

Wax resist princess

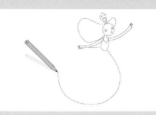

1. Using a pencil, draw the outline of a princess in a ballgown on a large piece of thick, white paper. Try not to press too hard.

The crayon lines are shown here in yellow so that you can see them.

2. Pressing quite hard, use a white wax crayon to draw frills and patterns on the ballgown. Then, draw some wavy lines or curls for the hair.

The crayon lines resist the paint.

3. Using a thick paintbrush, brush water all over the paper. Then, dip the brush in very watery paint and fill in the ballgown.

4. Add some blobs or swirls in a different shade of paint to parts of the ballgown. Allow the two shades of paint to bleed into each other.

5. Fill in the hair with more watery paint. Use a thinner paintbrush to paint the crown, face and arms. Then, add her legs and feet.

6. Leave the paint to dry completely. Then, use a sharp pencil to draw around the eyes. Draw lines for the nose and mouth, too.

Flag garland

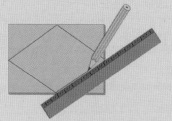

1. For a flag template, mark the middle points on each edge of a rectangle of cardboard. Join the dots, then cut out the shape.

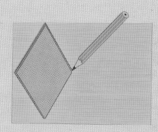

2. Place the cardboard template on some bright crêpe paper and draw around it in pencil. Then, cut out the shape.

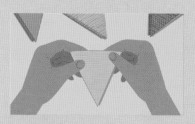

3. Make several flag shapes, in different shades of crêpe paper, in the same way. Then, fold them all in half, like this.

4. Cut out lots of small crowns, hearts, diamonds and fancy shapes. Then, glue the shapes to the fronts of the folded flags.

5. Cut out some even smaller shapes, such as diamonds and hearts, and glue them on top of the first ones. Then, unfold all the flags you have made.

6. Spread a flag with glue. Lay a piece of thread over the crease and fold the flag over it. Then, glue the rest of the flags onto the thread.

Bunny in a burrow

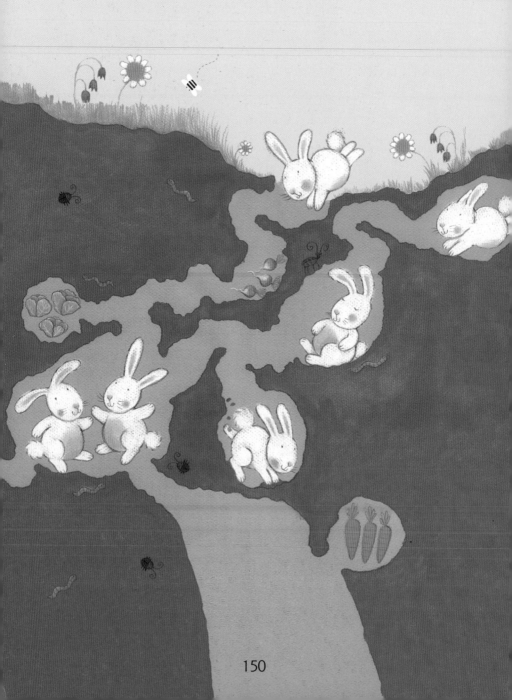

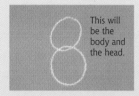

1. Use a white pencil to draw a circle on some brown paper. Draw an oval on top of the circle.

2. Draw two ears. Add shapes for the arms and legs. Draw a little circle for the tail. Fill in the body.

3. Use a pencil to draw around the head, ears, arm and back. Add little lines around the tail.

4. Draw a curved shape for the front leg. Draw around the tummy, the other leg and the other arm.

5. Add dots for eyes, a "V" for the nose, a curved mouth, whiskers and little lines on the paws.

6. Fill in the nose with a pink pencil. Then, add patches inside the ears and fill in the tummy.

7. Draw a wavy shape for a burrow around the bunny. Paint around the burrow with brown paint.

8. When the paint is dry, use different shades of pencils to draw worms and bugs in the soil.

Bug friends

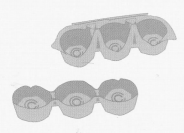

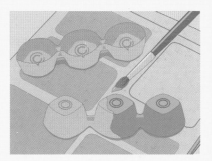

1. Cut the lid off a cardboard egg carton. Then, use scissors to cut the bottom part of the carton into two pieces, along its length.

2. For the caterpillars' bodies, lay the pieces of egg carton on an old newspaper. Brush them with thick green paint, then let them dry.

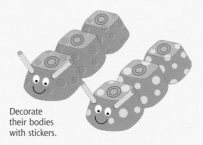

Decorate their bodies with stickers.

3. Using a ballpoint pen, carefully make two holes in the front of each caterpillar. Then, cut two short pieces from a drinking straw.

4. Push one piece of straw through each hole. Cut out white circles for eyes and glue them on. Then, draw the caterpillars' faces.

Bat card

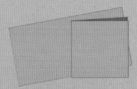

1. Cut two rectangles of thick paper. Fold one rectangle in half, short sides together. Crease the fold well.

2. Make two cuts in the folded side. Fold over the flap between the two cuts. Crease it well.

3. Turn the card over. Fold the flap again. Crease it well, then unfold it and open the card.

4. Pinch along the middle fold, on either side of the flap, like this, but don't pinch the flap.

5. Push the flap down into the card. Then, close the card and smooth all the folds flat.

6. Open the card. The flap should pop up like a box. Fold the other rectangle and glue it to the back.

7. Cut out a piece of black paper for the bat. Make sure that it fits inside the card, like this.

8. Draw the outline of a bat on the paper and cut it out. Dab glue on the box and press on the bat.

Fairy collage

1. Cut out pages with lots of different pictures of pretty flowers from old magazines. Then, cut around lots of flowers and leaves, too.

2. Glue the flowers onto a piece of paper. Make some of the flowers overlap and leave spaces between some of them for the fairies.

3. Draw the top part of a fairy's face peeking out over the top of a flower. Add the eyes and nose, then draw the hair, too.

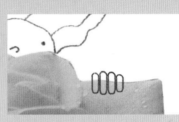

4. For fingers, draw four long ovals, touching each other. Make them overlap the flower to look as if they are curling over the petal.

5. You could also draw a fairy looking around the side of a flower. Just draw part of her body – the rest of it is hidden behind the flower.

6. When you have drawn fairies between the flowers, fill them in with pens or paints. Then, draw around them with a black pen.

Cut-out clowns

1. Cut a triangle from bright paper for the body. Cut two smaller triangles for arms and glue them onto the back.

2. Cut a circle for the head and glue it to the top of the body. Then, cut a shape for a hat and glue it onto the head.

3. For the clown's hair, cut two funny shapes from paper. Glue one piece of hair onto each side of the head.

4. Cut out hands and legs from paper and glue them on. Then, glue them to the back of the clown.

5. To make striped socks, cut little strips of paper and glue them onto the legs. Glue on two big clown shoes, too.

6. Use felt-tip pens to draw the clown's face. Then, decorate his hat, body and shoes with shapes cut from paper.

Cartoon cats

1. Using watery paints, mix a shade of orange. Paint a rough oval for the cat's body.

2. Mix a brighter shade of orange for stripes on the cat's body. Paint them while the paint is still damp.

3. When the paint is dry, outline it with a fine felt-tip pen. Add lines for the legs, and paws with claws.

4. Draw a face, long whiskers and a curly tail. For more ideas on painting cats, see below.

Finger puppet

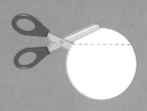

Hold the cone until it sticks.

1. Lay a mug on a piece of white paper. Draw around the mug, then cut out the circle.

2. Cut a piece, the width of two of your fingers, off the circle, to make a straight edge.

3. Spread glue halfway along the straight edge, then bend it around to make a cone.

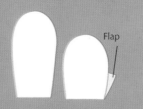

Flap

4. Draw a nose, some whiskers and two eyes on the cone's pointed end with felt-tip pens.

5. Cut two long ears out of the paper you cut off the circle. Fold their ends over, to make flaps.

6. Draw pink shapes in the middle of the ears. Spread glue on the flaps and press them onto the cone.

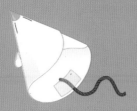

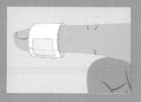

7. Cut a piece of black thread for the tail. Then, tape the tail inside the cone.

8. Cut a narrow strip of paper and wrap it around your finger. Then, tape it in place.

9. Dab a blob of glue on the rolled strip of paper and press it inside the mouse.

Zigzag castle card

1. Fold a long rectangle of thick paper in half. Then, fold the top layer in half again, like this.

Middle fold —

2. Turn the paper over, fold it in the same way, then unfold it. Cut off the left-hand part.

Keep both pieces.

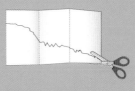

3. Using a pencil, draw a wavy line diagonally across the card, like this. Cut along the line.

Use a thin paintbrush.

4. Paint the right-hand part of the folded card green. When it is dry, paint tiny flowers on it.

5. Use purple paint to add mountains. When they are dry, outline the peaks with a silver pen.

6. Turn the card over and paint the middle part green. Cut out green paper trees and glue them on.

7. Paint a castle on the paper from step 2. Let it dry, then outline it with black pen, and cut it out.

8. Fold the paper into a zigzag again. Then, glue the castle near the top of the mountains.

You could make a castle like this one instead.

165

Flowery boxes

1. Cut or rip lots of shapes from bright tissue paper. Then, spread white glue on them and press them all over a box.

2. Cut lots of pictures of different kinds of flowers from old magazines. Cut as close to the edges of the flowers as you can.

3. Brush white glue onto the back of one of the paper flowers. Then, place the flower on the top of the box, like this.

4. Gently rub the flower, to make it really flat. Then, glue another flower onto the box, a little way from the first one.

The glue will be clear when it dries.

5. Glue on lots more flowers. Glue some of them so that they go over the edges of the box. Then, press them down.

6. Brush a thick layer of white glue over the whole box, including the flowers. Then, leave the glue to dry completely.

Snowflake fairies

1. Draw around a mug on white paper, then draw around it again on purple paper. Then, cut out the circles.

2. Carefully fold the white circle in half, then fold it twice more. Then, cut a triangle from one side.

3. Cut out lots more triangles, all around the edges of the folded paper. Then, unfold the snowflake.

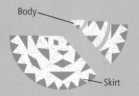

Body

Skirt

Sash

4. Brush white glue over the snowflake. Sprinkle it with glitter and let it dry. Glue it to the purple circle.

5. Cut the snowflake in half. From one of the halves, cut shapes for a skirt and a body, like this.

6. Glue the skirt onto a piece of paper, then glue on the body. Cut a purple sash and glue it on.

Fold

Keep the paper folded.

Add a crown and shoes, too.

7. For wings, cut out another circle and fold it as in step 2. Draw half a wing shape on the fold.

8. Cut out the wing shape. Cut triangles into the fold. Open out the wings, then spread glue on them.

9. Sprinkle glitter on the wings. Glue them on, then cut out and glue on the head, hair, legs and arms.

Heart garland

1. Cut a long, thin strip of green paper. Then, fold it in half, with the short ends together, like this. Crease the fold really well with your fingertip.

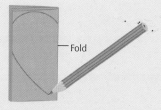

Fold

2. Fold the paper in half two more times. Then, draw half a heart on the folded paper, against the fold. Make the heart touch both edges.

Don't cut this part.

3. Draw a second line inside the first one, like this. Then, holding all the layers together, carefully cut along both of the lines.

Flatten the garland.

4. Carefully open out the garland and lay it on an old newspaper. Then, mix some paint and white glue together on an old plate.

5. Paint stripes on one of the hearts. Sprinkle glitter over the wet paint. Then, paint around another heart and sprinkle it with glitter.

6. Shake any excess glitter onto the newspaper. Glue sequins or paper shapes onto the other hearts, then leave the garland to dry.

Beaky bird card

1. Fold a piece of stiff paper in half, with its short ends together. Crease the fold well, then open it out again.

2. Draw a bird's body on some bright paper. Tear it out carefully and glue it to the middle of the card.

3. Tear out some wings and glue them to the sides of the body. Fold the card again and crease it well.

Crayon the inside, too.

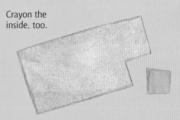

4. Cut the corner off an old envelope to make the beak. Then, brighten the beak with crayons or pens.

5. Glue the beak in the middle of the fold. Lift the top of the beak, then close the card, to flatten the beak.

6. Cut out two eyes and glue them on. Draw the legs and some feet. Then, glue flowers around the bird.

173

Cress shapes

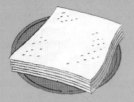

1. Pile ten paper towels onto a large flat plate or a plastic tray.

2. Pour some water onto the towels until they are soaking wet.

3. Lay some cookie cutters on the towels and spread them out.

4. Carefully sprinkle lots of cress or alfalfa seeds into each shape.

5. Spread out the seeds. Hold each cutter as you do this.

6. Carefully lift off the cutters. Put the plate or tray in a light place.

You can use any shape or size of cutter.

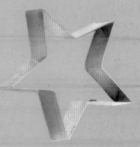

7. Water around the seeds every day, but don't put water on the seeds themselves.

8. When the plants are as long as your little finger, cut them with scissors and eat them.

175

Chalky landscape

1. For the sky, rub the side of a blue chalk pastel on a piece of paper. Leave a space for the trees.

2. Add some patches of pale blue pastel to the sky. Then, add darker blue pastel over the top.

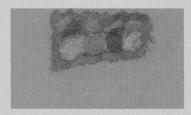

3. Use the side of an orange pastel to fill in a tree. Fill in the other trees with red and yellow pastels.

4. Add lots of diagonal lines on each tree with dark and light pastels. Let the lines overlap.

5. Use the side of green, yellow and orange pastels to create striped fields below the trees, like this.

6. Using the end of a black pastel, draw a line along the top of the fields. Add tree trunks and branches.

Flower gift tags

1. Wet a sheet of paper thoroughly, then shake off any drips. Lay it flat on a piece of plastic foodwrap.

2. Dab on blobs of paint to make petals. The paint will bleed and spread across the wet sheet of paper.

3. Add a contrasting blob of paint to each petal, a black blob in the middle and green blobs for the leaves.

4. Leave the paper to dry completely. Don't move it before it is dry, or the paint will run.

5. Roughly cut around the flowers, then glue them onto thin cardboard. Leave the glue to dry.

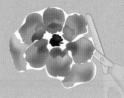

6. Cut out the flowers, leaving a thin white border around the edges. Then, tape on pieces of gift ribbon.

Glitter bugs

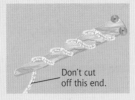

Don't cut off this end.

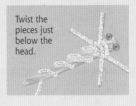

Twist the pieces just below the head.

1. Cut a foil square as large as your hand and roll it. Flatten one end and glue on sequins for eyes.

2. Wind a pipe cleaner along the body, like this. Leave the extra part at the end of the body.

3. Cut another pipe cleaner in half. Twist each half around the body. Then, bend the ends out, like this.

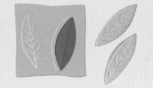

4. For wings, lay a leaf on newspaper, with its veins facing up. Brush it with silver or gold paint.

5. Using the leaf, print four wings onto two shades of tissue paper. When they are dry, cut them out.

6. Lay the wings, painted side down. Carefully place the bug on top, upside down, like this.

The foil should be long enough to cover the stick.

7. Tape the pipe cleaners onto the wings. Then, bend the pipe cleaners to open the wings.

8. Tape the end of a strip of foil to one end of a kebab stick. Wrap the foil around it, then tape it.

9. Lay the blunt end of the stick next to the body. Wind the extra pipe cleaner around the stick.

Patterned eggs

Wax patterns

The wax resists the food dye.

1. Use a wax crayon to draw patterns on a hard-boiled egg. Then, put 3-4 teaspoons of bright food dye into a glass.

Leave it for ten minutes.

2. Half fill the glass with water, then put the egg into the glass. Using a spoon, turn the egg until it is covered with the dye.

3. When the egg is bright enough, lift it out of the glass with a spoon. Then, place it on a paper towel to dry completely.

Stickers

Make sure the egg is dry.

1. Press tiny stickers all over a hard-boiled egg. Use shiny ones if possible, because they don't soak up so much of the dye.

2. Put the egg in a glass of food dye, as you did before. Then, lift the egg out with a spoon and put it on a paper towel to dry.

3. When the egg is completely dry, carefully peel off the stickers. You'll see pale shapes where the stickers were before.

Store the eggs in a refrigerator and eat them within three days.

Blow painted trees

1. Dip a paintbrush into bright ink and paint a big blob on a piece of white paper, for the tree trunk.

2. Hold a drinking straw above the ink. Blow through the straw, to 'chase' the ink up the paper for a trunk.

3. Then, use the end of the straw to pull a few thin lines of ink away from the trunk.

4. Blow the lines of ink with the straw to make branches. Then, blow some thinner branches, too.

5. For the leaves, mix orange ink with some water. Dab the watery ink over the branches again and again.

6. Mix some more watery orange ink and paint grass around the bottom of the tree, like this.

Painted shrimps

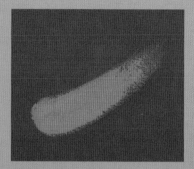

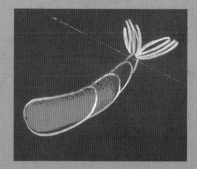

1. Dip a thick paintbrush into some red paint and paint a curved line. Lift your brush up quickly at the end.

2. When the paint is dry, draw around the body with a white pencil. Add body segments and a tail.

3. Draw several lines at the head end of the body for feelers. Then, add two very long lines, curving out.

4. Draw several short curved lines along the body for the legs. Then, add an eye with a black felt-tip pen.

Flower bracelet

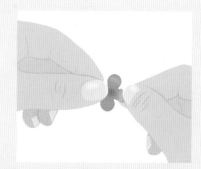

1. Cut a long piece of narrow ribbon that goes once around your wrist, with a little extra for tying on the bracelet.

2. Draw three hearts and two flowers on pieces of bright paper. Cut them out, then bend the petals with your fingers, like this.

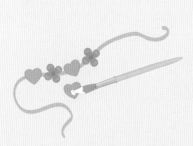

3. Using white glue, glue one heart onto the middle of the ribbon. Glue a flower on either side, then glue on the other hearts.

4. Glue a sequin in the middle of each flower. Then, when the glue is dry, ask someone to tie the bracelet around your wrist.

Oil pastel lizard

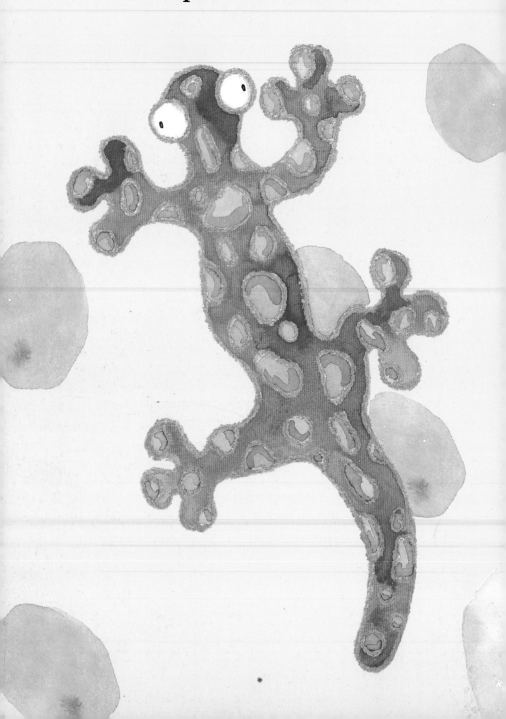

1. Draw a faint outline of a lizard with a pencil. Then, draw over the outline with a bright oil pastel.

2. Draw spots and blobs all over the lizard, like this. Make sure that all parts of the body are covered.

3. Dip a thin paintbrush into some bright ink, then carefully fill in the lizard's body, around the spots.

4. Fill in the spots with another bright shade of ink. The pastel outline will stop the ink from spreading.

5. Use a black felt-tip pen to add middles onto the eyes. Then, paint some 'stones' around the lizard.

Fairy bookmark

1. Cut a circle from paper for the fairy's head. Then, lay the head on some pink paper and draw a shape for the hair. Cut the hair out.

2. Cover the hair with glue and sprinkle it with glitter. While the glue dries, cut a strip from the pink paper and glue the head onto it.

3. Glue the hair onto the fairy's head and draw a face with pens and pencils. Then, cut a crown from shiny paper and glue it onto the hair.

4. For wings, fold a piece of thick paper in half and draw a wing on it, like this. Then, keeping the paper folded, cut out the shape.

5. Glue the wings onto the back of the pink strip of paper. Then, decorate the bookmark with stickers, glitter glue and gold pens.

Springy things

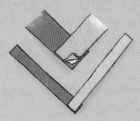

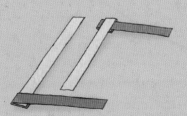

1. Glue the end of a yellow strip of paper over the end of a red one, to make a right angle. Lay the strips on a table in a V-shape.

2. Fold the red strip across the end of the yellow strip and crease it. Then, fold the yellow strip down across the red strip in the same way.

Tab

3. Continue folding the red and yellow strips across one another so that they make a spring. Keep folding until you run out of paper.

4. Glue down the last whole yellow flap and trim it to fit. Fold over the extra paper on the red strip to make a tab, like this.

5. Draw a picture on some white cardboard and cut it out. Glue it onto the red tab. Glue the other end of the spring inside a gift box.

Hatching chick card

Use bright giftwrap with a small pattern.

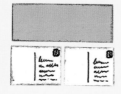

1. Take a piece of thick paper. Cut it to the length of about two postcards.

2. Fold the paper in half, short sides together. Open the paper out.

3. Fold the short sides in, so that they meet at the middle fold. Crease the folds.

Make the egg slightly smaller than the card.

Glue the egg across the middle of the card.

Don't cut the back of the card.

4. Draw an egg on the back of some giftwrap, then carefully cut it out.

5. Carefully glue the egg onto the card. Draw a zigzag from top to bottom.

6. Pull the front and back of the card apart carefully, then cut along the zigzag.

7. Draw a chick shape on a piece of yellow paper. Cut it out. Add a beak and eyes.

8. Carefully glue the paper chick over the fold in the middle of the card.

9. Draw legs with a felt-tip pen. Then, decorate the inside of the card.

Bunny napkin rings

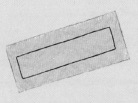

1. Fold a stiff piece of paper, the length of your hand, in half. Draw half the shape of a bunny's head.

2. Cut around the shape of the head. Open out the paper and use felt-tip pens to draw a face.

3. For the body, draw a rectangle on a piece of thick paper. Make it twice the length of your hand.

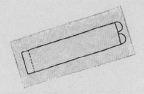

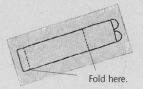

Fold here.

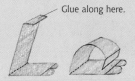

Glue along here.

4. Add two bumps at one end for the feet. Draw a dotted line a little way in from the other end.

5. Draw another line about a hand's length along. Cut out the shape. Fold it along the dotted lines.

6. Put some glue along the short edge and curve the paper over. Stick the edge behind the feet.

To bend a bunny's ear, roll it around a pencil.

7. Turn the head over and put two blobs of glue below the ears. Press the head onto the body.

8. For a tail, pull a piece off a cotton ball. Roll it into a ball and glue it on the back of the body.

199

Sparkly wand

1. Draw a star on a piece of cardboard. Cut it out, then lay it on another piece of cardboard and draw around it twice.

2. Cut out the stars and paint them on one side. Then, cut 10 pieces of thin ribbon that are half as long as a drinking straw.

3. Lay one of the stars on a piece of scrap paper. Then, spread white glue over the side that has not been painted, like this.

4. Carefully lay the straw and the pieces of ribbon on top of the glue, like this. Then, spread glue on the other star and lay it on top.

The paper protects the book.

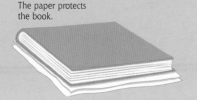

5. Lay a sheet of paper over the star. Then, put a heavy book on top, and leave the wand for an hour, until the glue is completely dry.

6. Glue lots of sequins, glitter and tiny beads onto one side of the wand. Wait for the glue to dry, then decorate the other side, too.

Dinosaur eggs

1. Mix lots of watery pale yellow paint. Then, paint a patch for the dinosaurs' nest on a large piece of white paper. Leave it to dry.

2. Mix some stronger shades of orangey-yellow paint. Then, paint lots of ovals for the eggs. Make one or two of the ovals overlap.

Use a thin black pen.

3. Mix some orange paint, then paint a line above an egg for a dinosaur's neck. Add an oval for a head, then let the paint dry.

4. Draw around the head and neck, then add eyes, a mouth and a frill. Draw the shell outline and zigzags for the broken edge at the top.

You could add feet on either side of the head. Draw a piece of shell on top, too.

5. Draw zigzag lines coming from the broken edge for a crack on the shell. Add lots of little dots and circles on the shell, too.

Index

Written by Fiona Watt, Rebecca Gilpin,
Leonie Pratt, Anna Milbourne, Ruth Brocklehurst,
Stephanie Turnbull and Ben Denne.

Designed & illustrated by Antonia Miller, Non Figg,
Amanda Gulliver, Jan McCafferty, Lucy Parris,
Russell Punter, Katrina Fearn, Rachel Wells,
Doriana Berkovic, Molly Sage and Andi Good.

Pg. 166 Images of flowers © Digital Vision

This edition published in 2012 by Usborne Publishing Ltd,
83-85 Saffron Hill, London, EC1N 8RT, England. www.usborne.com
Copyright © 2012, 2009, 1995 Usborne Publishing Ltd.
The name Usborne and the devices ♀ ⊕ are Trade Marks of Usborne
Publishing Ltd. All rights reserved. No part of this publication may be
reproduced, stored in a retrieval system, or transmitted in any form or
by any means, electronic, mechanical, photocopying, recording or
otherwise without the prior permission of the publisher. UE.
First published in America in 2012.
Printed in Shenzhen, Guangdong, China.